KALMUS MINATURE ORCHESTRA SCORES

No. F 253

BELA BARTOK

STRING QUARTET No. 1
OPUS 7

EDWIN F. KALMUS
PUBLISHER OF MUSIC
NEW YORK, N. Y.

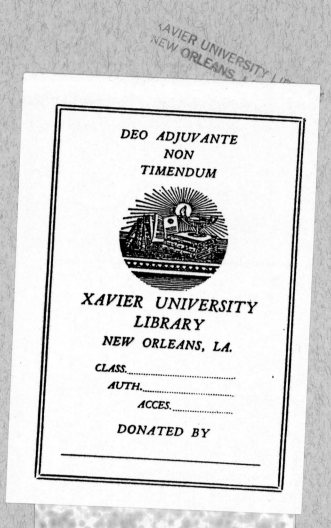

KALMUS MINIATURE ORCHESTRA SCORES

BELA
BARTOK

STRING QUARTET No. 1
OPUS 7

EDWIN F. KALMUS
PUBLISHER OF MUSIC
NEW YORK, N. Y.

BELA BARTOK, STRING QUARTET NO. I, OP. 7

BELA BARTOK, STRING QUARTET NO. I, OP. 7

KALMUS MINIATURE ORCHE[illegible]RES

All Kalmus Scores Are Printed in U. S. A.

BACH
- No. 72. Suite No. 2 in B minor .... $ .50
- No. 143. Concerto for 2 Violins in D minor ... .60
- No. 152. High Mass in B minor 3.00
- F 176. St. Matthew's Passion 2.50
- F 316. St. John's Passion 2.50
- F 319. Magnificat 1.00
- No. 120. Brandenburg Concerto No. 1 in F major .... .50
- No. 121. Brandenburg Concerto No. 2 in F major .... .60
- No. 122. Brandenburg Concerto No. 3 in G major .... .50
- No. 123. Brandenburg Concerto No. 4 in G major .... .65
- No. 124. Brandenburg Concerto No. 5 in D major .... .65
- No. 125. Brandenburg Concerto No. 6 in B flat major .... .50
- No. 160. The Musical Offering (Size 9x12) 2.50
- No. 180. The Art of the Fugue 3.00
- The Fugues of the Well Tempered Clavier, Vol. I, in open score 2.00

BARTOK
- F 320. String Quartet No. 1, op. 7, with Kodaly String Quartet, op. 2 ..... 1.00

BEETHOVEN
- No. 1. Symphony No. 1, op. 21 .... .75
- No. 2. Symphony No. 2, op. 36 .... 1.00
- No. 3. Symphony No. 3, op. 55 .... 1.25
- No. 4. Symphony No. 4, op. 60 .... 1.25
- No. 5. Symphony No. 5, op. 67 .... 1.25
- No. 6. Symphony No. 6, op. 68 (Pastorale) .. 1.25
- No. 7. Symphony No. 7, op. 92 .... 1.25
- No. 8. Symphony No. 8, op. 93 .... 1.25
- No. 57. Symphony No. 9 (Choral) 2.75
- F 309. Symphonies #1, #2, #3, #4—four score pages on one large page, 10 x 13¼", in 1 volume 2.00
- F 310. Symphonies #5, #6, #7—four score pages on one large page, 10 x 13¼", in one volume 2.00
- F 311. Symphonies #8, #9—four score pages on one large page, in 1 volume 2.00
- F 312. All Nine Symphonies—four score pages on one large page, in 1 volume 4.50
- F 302. Piano Concertos in one volume 2.25
- F 301. Violin Concerto, together with Brahms, Mendelssohn, Tschaikowsky Violin Concertos 2.25
- No. 128. String Quartets, op. 18/1-6 .... 2.50
- No. 129. String Quartets, op. 59, No. 1-3, op. 74, op. 95 .... 2.50
- No. 130. String Quartets, op. 127, 130, 131, 132, 133, 135 .... 3.00

(String Quartets separately)
- No. 230. F major op. 18/1 .... .45
- No. 231. G major op. 18/2 .... .40
- No. 232. D major op. 18/3 .... .40
- No. 233. C minor op. 18/4 .... .40
- No. 234. A major op. 18/5 .... .40
- No. 235. Bb major op. 18/6 .... .40
- No. 236. F major op. 59/1 .... .50
- No. 237. E minor op. 59/2 .... .45
- No. 238. C major op. 59/3 .... .45
- No. 239. Eb major op. 74 .... .45
- No. 240. F minor op. 95 .... .45
- No. 241. Eb major op. 127 .... .50
- No. 242. Bb major op. 130 .... .50

BEETHOVEN
- No. 243. C# minor op. 131 .... .50
- No. 244. A minor op. 132 .... .50
- No. 245. Bb major op. 133 .... .40
- No. 246. F major op. 135 .... .40
- No. 9. Lenore No. 3, Overture op. 72a .... .60
- No. 10. Prometheus, Overture, op. 42 .... .50
- No. 11. Coriolanus, Overture, op. 62 .... .50
- No. 67. Egmont, Overture, op. 84 .... .50

BERLIOZ
- No. 144. Fantastic Symphony, op. 14 .... 2.50
- No. 175. Three pieces from "Damnation of Faust" .... .75

BIZET
- No. 174. L'Arlesienne Suite No. 1 .... 1.00

BORODINE
- No. 68. Polovetzian Dances, Prince Igor 1.50
- No. 149. On the Steppes of Asia .... .60
- No. 166. Symphony No. 2 in B minor 3.00

BRAHMS
- No. 12. Symphony No. 1, op. 68 .... 1.25
- No. 14. Symphony No. 2, op. 73 .... 1.25
- No. 15. Symphony No. 3, op. 90 .... 1.25
- No. 16. Symphony No. 4, op. 98 .... 1.25
- No. 140. Haydn Variations, op. 56b .... .75
- F 313. Symphonies #1, #2—four score pages on one large page, 10 x 13¼", in 1 volume 1.50
- F 314. Symphonies #3, #4—four score pages on one large page, 10 x 13¼", in 1 volume 1.50
- F 315. All four Symphonies—four score pages on one large page, 10 x 13¼", in 1 volume 3.00
- F 300. 2 Piano Concertos, op. 15, op. 83, in one volume 2.00
- F 301. Violin Concerto, together with Beethoven, Mendelssohn, Tschaikowsky, Violin Concertos 2.25
- F 307. Chamber Music for strings 2.00

Contents: String Quartets op. 51 No. 1 & 2, op. 67, String Quintets op. 88, op 111, Clarinet Quintet op. 115, String Sextets op. 18, op. 36

BRUCKNER
- No. 158. Symphony No. 7, E major 2.50

CHABRIER
- No. 61. Espana, Rhapsody 1.25

CORELLI
- No. 136. Concerto Grosso, op. 6, No. 8, (Christmas Concerto) large size, 9 x 12 inches 1.25

DEBUSSY
- No. 17. Afternoon of a Faun 1.00
- No. 73. String Quartet 1.00
- No. 100. Nocturnes No. 1, Nuages .... .75
- No. 102. Nocturnes No. 3, Sirenes 1.25
- No. 103. Nocturnes, complete 2.50

DELIUS
- No. 250. Two pieces for small orchestra (On Hearing the First Cuckoo in Spring, Summernight on the River) 1.00

DVORAK
- No. 18. New World Symphony, No. 5, op. 95 . 1.50
- No. 90. String Quartet, op. 96 (American) .. .60
- No. 134. Carneval Overture, op. 92 .... 1.25
- No. 247. Serenade for strings op. 22 .... 1.50

All scores marked "F" before numbers are printed four score pages on a page 10" x 13¼", which is LARGER than the usual sheet music size. The actual size of the scores has been reduced only very little, as a trial will show; in fact, it would not be noticeable, if attention were not called to it. These scores do not contain any arrows, and are perfectly suited for score reading.

Always specify KALMUS EDITIONS at your dealers or when making up your requisitions.

KALMUS MINIATURE ORCHESTRA SCORES

All Kalmus Scores Are Printed in U. S. A.

DUKAS
- No. 65. The Sorcerer's Apprentice, size 9 x 12 inches 2.00

ENESCO
- No. 248. Second Roumanian Rhapsody op. 11/2 .... 1.50

FRANCK
- No. 19. Symphony in D minor 1.50

GLIERE
- No. 115. Russian Sailor's Dance from "The Red Poppy" 1.00

GRIEG
- No. 163. Piano Concerto in A minor, op. 16 size 9 x 12 inches 1.75
- No. 168. op. 40, Holberg Suite, size 9x12 inches 1.25
- No. 214A. Norwegian Dances, op. 35, size 9 x 12 inches 2.50
- F 304. Piano Concerto together with Schumann, Tschaikowsky Concertos 2.00

HAENDEL
- No. 159. The Messiah 5.00

HAYDN
- No. 24. Symphony No. 2, in D major (London) .60
- No. 25. Symphony No. 6, in G major (Surprise) .... .60
- No. 105. Symphony No. 88 (13) in G major .. 1.00
- No. 106. Symphony No. 4, in D major (Clock) . .75
- No. 108. Symphony No. 1, in Eb (Roll of the Kettledrum) .... .75
- No. 229. Toy Symphony, size 9 x 12 inches 1.25

30 CELEBRATED STRING QUARTETS
- No. 181. op. 3/3 in G major .... .40
- No. 182. op. 3/5 in F major .... .40
- No. 183. op. 9/2 in Eb major .... .40
- No. 184. op. 17/5 in G major .... .40
- No. 185. op. 20/4 in D major .... .40
- No. 186. op. 20/5 in F minor .... .40
- No. 187. op. 20/6 in A major .... .40
- No. 188. op. 33/2 in Eb major .... .40
- No. 189. op. 33/3 in C major .... .40
- No. 190. op. 33/6 in D major .... .40
- No. 191. op. 50/6 in D major .... .40
- No. 192. op. 54/1 in G major .... .40
- No. 193. op. 54/2 in C major .... .40
- No. 194. op. 54/3 in E major .... .40
- No. 195. op. 64/2 in B minor .... .40
- No. 196. op. 64/3 in Bb major .... .40
- No. 197. op. 64/4 in G major .... .40
- No. 198. op. 64/5 in D major .... .40
- No. 199. op. 64/6 in Eb major .... .40
- No. 200. op. 74/1 in C major .... .40
- No. 201. op. 74/2 in F major .... .40
- No. 202. op. 74/3 in G minor .... .40
- No. 203. op. 76/1 in G major .... .40
- No. 204. op. 76/2 in D minor .... .40
- No. 205. op. 76/3 in C major .... .40
- No. 206. op. 76/4 in Bb major .... .40
- No. 207. op. 76/5 in D major .... .40
- No. 208. op. 76/6 in Eb major .... .40
- No. 209. op. 77/1 in G major .... .40
- No. 210. op. 77/2 in F major .... .40
- Nos. 211, 212, 213 the above 30 string quartets bound into 3 volumes—each volume . 4.00

KALINNIKOW
- No. 171. Symphony No. 1 .... 5.00

KODALY
- F 320. String Quartet No. 1, op. 2, together with Bartok String Quartet No. 1 ... 1.00

LIADOFF, A.
- No. 109. Music Box .... .40

LISZT
- No. 29. Les Preludes 1.00

MAHLER
- No. 154. Symphony No. 2 in C minor 4.00

McKAY
- Sinfonietta No. 4 .... 2.50

MENDELSSOHN
- No. 30. Midsummer Night's Dream, Ov. .... .50
- No. 32. Wedding March .... .30
- No. 31. Hebrides (Fingal's Cave), Ov. .... .65
- No. 81. Three Orchestra pieces from Midsummer Night's Dream .... .50
- No. 145. Violin Concerto, op. 64, E minor 1.00
- No. 117. Symphony No. 3 in A minor op. 56 (Scotch) 1.50
- No. 126. Symphony No. 4 in A major, op 80 (Italian) 1.50
- F 301. Violin Concerto, together with Beethoven, Brahms, Tschaikowsky 2.25

MOZART
- No. 33. Symphony No. 39, in E flat, K 543 ... .75
- No. 34. Symphony No. 40 in G minor K 550 . .75
- No. 35. Symphony No. 41, in C major (Jupiter), K 551 .... .75
- No. 69. Don Juan, Overture, K 457 .... .40
- No. 70. Marriage of Figaro, Overture .... .40
- No. 71. Magic Flute, Overture, K 620 .... .40
- No. 80. Serenade, Kleine Nachtmusik, K 525 .35
- No. 150. La Finta Giardiniera, Ouv. .... .40
- No. 151. Prelude to Il Re Pastore .... .40
- No. 171A. Symphony in C major, K 200 ...... .75
- No. 173. Symphony in D major (Haffner), K 385 .... .85
- No. 179. Requiem 3.50
- F 305. Three Violin Concertos K216, K218, K219 .... 1.25
- F 306. Four Serenades and Two Divertimenti K251, 334, 286, 361, 375, 388 .... 2.00
- F 303. Five Piano Concertos, K466, 467, 488, 491, 595 .... 2.25
- No. 214. Clarinet Quintet, K 581 .... .75
- No. 218. String quartet in G major, K 387 ... .40
- No. 219. String quartet in D minor, K 421 ... .40
- No. 220. String quartet in Eb major, K 428 ... .40
- No. 221. String quartet in Bb major, K 458 ... .40
- No. 222. String quartet in A major, K 464 ... .40
- No. 223. String quartet in C major, K 465 ... .40
- No. 224. String quartet in D major, K 499 ... .40
- No. 225. String quartet in D major, K 575 ... .40
- No. 226. String quartet in Bb major, K 589 ... .40
- No. 227. String quartet in F major, K 590 ... .40
- No. 228. All 10 string quartets bound in a volume 4.00

MUSSORGSKY
- No. 83. Polonaise from Boris Godunow ..... .75

NICOLAI
- No. 217. Merry Wives of Windsor Ouv. 1.00

PROKOFIEFF
- No. 164. Classic Symphony 2.25
- No. 249. Symphony #5 .... 3.00

All scores marked "F" before numbers are printed four score pages on a page 10" x 13¼", which is LARGER than the usual sheet music size. The actual size of the scores has been reduced only very little, as a trial will show; in fact, it would not be noticeable, if attention were not called to it. These scores do not contain any arrows, and are perfectly suited for score reading.

Always specify KALMUS EDITIONS at your dealers or when making up your requisitions.